Amy Cooper

Holly Avenue

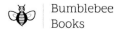
Bumblebee
Books

BUMBLEBEE PAPERBACK EDITION

A CIP catalogue record for this title is
available from the British Library.

ISBN: 978-1-83934-387-2

This is a work of fiction.
Names, characters, places and incidents originate from the writer's imagination. Any resemblance
to actual persons, living or dead, is purely coincidental.

First Published in 2022

Olympia Publishers
Tallis House
2 Tallis Street
London
EC4Y 0AB

Printed in Great Britain

Holly Avenue

Dedication

To my loves, Max, Murray and Meade

It was almost 3 o'clock in the afternoon when the new neighbours arrived. It was about the same time my favourite Christmas film was starting and Mum had given my brothers and me the biggest popcorn soup I had ever seen.

A car carefully drove into the driveway of the empty house opposite, followed by a bright red lorry that blocked the whole road and my view from the window.

I was so unbelievably excited to have new neighbours after Mr White had moved out last week. He'd gone to live with his family in the next town after living here for 47 years.

I was sure the new family would be just as happy here as he was.

We lived on the happiest road in our town, especially at

Christmas.

Even its name was Christmassy, Holly Avenue.

Christmas was kind of our thing on Holly Avenue.

Every house was decorated in sparkling lights that twinkled proudly all night. Wreaths hung on doors and snowmen were positioned in front gardens.

As I watched the movie I started to wonder about the new family that had moved into number 25 that day. Mum had already told me that there was a girl my age and a Mum and a Dad but she didn't know much more than that.

The lorry was still there at bedtime.

It was a bit fancy for a moving lorry, it was a bit fancy for any lorry. It glittered under the fairy lights of Holly Avenue and had little reindeer on each of the wheels that appeared to gallop as the lorry drove away the following morning.

I had woken up early to sit by the window again. As I watched the red lorry drive away, I inched closer to the glass, waiting for a glimpse of the new neighbours.

I sat there all morning until I saw a curtain twitch.

My heart jumped and before I knew it, I was waving frantically. I waved and smiled, smiled and waved but still, no one was there.

I needed something to catch their eye. I headed straight to my craft supplies and made a paper star to hang in our window out of some brown paper bags we often used for snacks.

That was sure to make them look. I finished before bath time and hung my paper star in the centre of our window.

Holly Avenue

HollyAvenue

The next morning, I ran downstairs to look out of the window at the new neighbour's house. I ran so fast that I thought I might still be dreaming when I saw a star hanging in their window too! Just like the one I had made.

"We have contact"

I shrieked.

I couldn't believe it, they must have loved my star and made their own.

"They are trying to communicate!"

I yelled up at Mum, who was still in bed.

What could I make next? I wondered as I brushed my teeth, combed my hair and put on my second to first favourite Christmas jumper, the one with the pom-poms on.

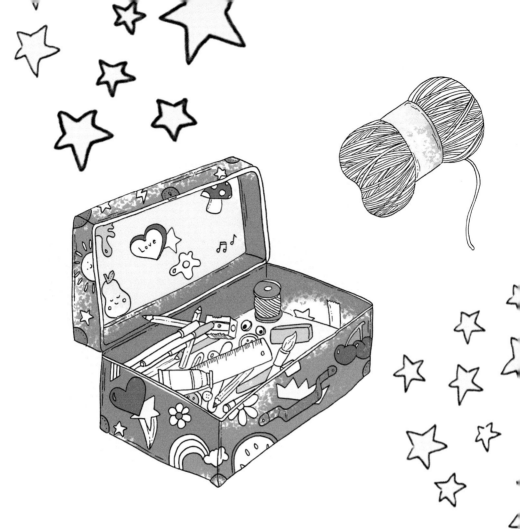

"Pom-poms! That's it!"

I declared loudly.

Luckily, I had some yarn in my trusted craft supply box and began working on a pom pom garland that would drape the length of the window. I chose white yarn in the hope it would look like falling snowballs.

By lunchtime, I had finished my garland with a little help from Mum. Dad hung it up and we headed out for some hot chocolate and a leaf hunt in the woods.

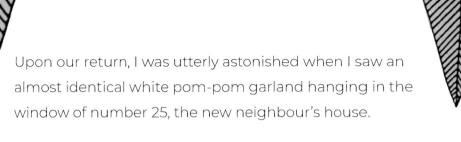

Upon our return, I was utterly astonished when I saw an almost identical white pom-pom garland hanging in the window of number 25, the new neighbour's house.

"Please can we knock on their door"
I begged Mum

"Not now darling, it's three sleeps until Christmas and I need some help with wrapping your grandparents presents"
Mum replied.

I had to agree, of course, I had been good all year and there was no way I was about to blow it with Father Christmas this close to Christmas Eve.

On the floor by the fire, we listened to Mum's favourite music, Michael Bublé whilst wrapping presents and tying bows until the beautiful gifts were carefully placed under the tree.

When we finished Mum told me I could keep the leftover ribbon and paper for my craft box.

What could I make with such small squares of wrapping paper I thought, looking out of the window in the direction of number 25.

The house looked quiet. The curtains had been closed since the new neighbours moved in and other than the twitch, I hadn't seen any signs of movement. Number 25 was a pretty house, it had a tree in the back garden that towered high above all the houses in the whole of Holly Avenue.

"Trees"

This time I would make origami trees for the window and before you could say "rocking around the Christmas tree" I had made 5 beautiful green and gold origami trees that were sure to put smiles on the new neighbour's faces.

The small Christmas trees were balanced on the window ledge, all was quiet in the house and I was fast asleep in bed dreaming of gingerbread when...

"Two sleeps until Christmas"

My brothers screamed as they thundered down the stairs for breakfast

I bolted upright, rubbed my eyes and smiled wide.

The first thing I did when I arrived downstairs was to head to the window where I was sure I would see 5 origami trees in the window mirroring ours.

"THIS IS AMAZING"

There were not 5 but 1, 2, 3, 4, 5, 6, 7, 8, trees in the window I was staring into and there again, was the curtain twitch, just as I had seen before.

How I wish they would show their faces.

HollyAvenue

It was wet and miserable outside, a perfect day for surveillance and drawing.

I decided I would stay by the window all day, most of the day, well as long as I could. I gathered my craft box and perched on the corner of the sofa.

So far, I had made a star, a snowball pom-pom garland and 5 origami Christmas trees. The window was starting to look a bit like our street.

"Holly Avenue"

I gasped, delighted I had some inspiration for the next part of my window display.

I used my special white glass pen to draw Holly Avenue on our window, drawing houses next to each other, with their snowmen and string lights swaying from house to house.

My hand hurt by the time I had finished but it looked amazing. I was bursting for the neighbours to see it and hoped they would copy it, just as they had with the other decorations.

Once again, I found myself in bed, eager and excited, waiting for morning to come.

I was dreaming about singing brussels sprouts when I was suddenly woken from my sleep. As I rubbed my tired eyes I realised, I could still hear the singing. The faint sounds of "Jingle bells" was coming from across the road.

I peered through the gap in my bedroom window curtains.

Opposite I could see a stunning display of white houses on the new neighbour's front window. It was beautiful, they had added a message that read Merry Christmas and my heart warmed as if I had drunk warm milk or eaten a toasted marshmallow without blowing on it first.

Holly Avenue

I stood there listening to the sweet soft music, looking at every detail in the wonderful window for a few moments then tiptoed into my parent's bedroom. Gently shaking my Mum and Dad until they too were awake, I told them about the noise outside and the message on the window.

Leaving my brothers fast asleep my Mum, Dad and I took the squeaky journey down the stairs into the living room where together we wrote 'With Love' on our window and snuggled on the sofa together, the music singing us into a deep sleep.

HollyAvenue

"It's Christmas Eve"

echoed my brothers jumping on the three of us.

Through tired eyes, we all looked outside and from the window opposite, stood a family staring back with happy faces and matching Christmas pyjamas waving and smiling, smiling and waving.

I noticed something in the corner of my eye, it was house number 21, a couple of doors down. It was the Campbells waving in their window, with three stars, and some pom-poms and some glittery baubles hanging from their curtain pole.

Our friends at number 14 were waving from their house too. They had decorated their window in ribbon as if their window were a huge present.

The more we looked, the more of the wonderful neighbours we saw, each with festively decorated windows, all waving, all smiling.

What a wonderful Christmas it would be for Holly Avenue.

Holly Avenue

WELCOME

Holly Avenue

Holly Avenue

About the Author

Amy Cooper grew up with a childhood free of youtube, navigated teen years to a soundtrack of Indy and 90's house music and spent her early twenties in the City recruiting IT hotshots and sweating on the tube. Now, in her thirties Amy lives in Berkhamsted, Hertfordshire, with her husband, three children and beloved French Bulldog. She believes in providing her children with opportunities to fulfil their dreams which lead to her realising her own, to write. You can find Amy at her desk, sewing machine or on the school run.